Family and Guests,

Join us in a grand memorial

&

celebration of the life of our beloved

{
It is not
length
of life,

but

depth
of life

}

-Ralph Waldo Emerson

Name

Comments

Name

Comments

Name

Comments

Name

Comments

Name   *Comments*

_____   _____

_____   _____

_____   _____

_____   _____

_____   _____

_____   _____

_____   _____

_____   _____

_____   _____

_____   _____

_____   _____

_____   _____

_____   _____

_____

_____

Name

Comments

Name

Comments

Name

Comments

Name

Comments

Name

Comments

Name

Comments

Name

Comments

Name

Comments

Name

Comments

Name

Comments

Name

Comments

Name

Comments

Name

Comments

Name

Comments

_____

_____

_____

_____

_____

_____

_____

_____

_____

_____

_____

_____

_____

_____

_____

_____

_____

_____

_____

_____

_____

_____

_____

_____

_____

_____

Name

Comments

Name

Comments

Name

Comments

Name

Comments

Name

Comments

Name

_____

_____

_____

_____

_____

_____

_____

_____

_____

Comments

_____

_____

_____

_____

_____

_____

_____

_____

_____

_____

_____

_____

_____

_____

_____

_____

_____

_____

Name

Comments

Name

Comments

Name

Comments

Name

Comments

Name

Comments

Name

Comments

Name

Comments

Name

Comments

Name

Comments

Name

_____

_____

_____

_____

_____

_____

_____

_____

_____

Comments

_____

_____

_____

_____

_____

_____

_____

_____

_____

_____

_____

_____

_____

_____

_____

_____

_____

Name

_____

_____

_____

_____

_____

_____

_____

_____

_____

Comments

_____

_____

_____

_____

_____

_____

_____

_____

_____

_____

_____

_____

_____

_____

_____

_____

_____

_____

Name

Comments

Name

Comments

Name

Comments

Name

Comments

Name

Comments

Name

Comments

Name

Comments

Name

Comments

Name

Comments

Name

Comments

Name

Comments

Name

Comments

Name

Comments

Name

Comments